3 Lions' +11 Great Sports Themes

Your Guarantee of Quality

As publishers, we strive to produce every book to the highest commercial standards.

The music has been freshly engraved and the book has been carefully designed to minimise awkward page turns and to make playing from it a real pleasure.

Particular care has been given to specifying acid-free, neutral-sized paper made from pulps which have not been elemental chlorine bleached. This pulp is from farmed sustainable forests and was produced with special regard for the environment.

Throughout, the printing and binding have been planned to ensure a sturdy, attractive publication which should give years of enjoyment.

If your copy fails to meet our high standards, please inform us and we will gladly replace it.

Music Sales' complete catalogue describes thousands of titles and is available in full colour sections by subject, direct from Music Sales Limited. Please state your areas of interest and send a cheque/postal order for £1.50 for postage to: Music Sales Limited, Newmarket Road, Bury St. Edmunds, Suffolk IP33 3YB.

Visit the Internet Music Shop at
http://www.musicsales.co.uk

Exclusive Distributors:
Music Sales Limited
8-9 Frith Street, London W1V 5TZ, England
Music Sales Pty Limited
120 Rothschild Avenue, Rosebery, NSW 2018, Australia

Order No.AM954063
ISBN 0-7119-7215-X
This book © Copyright 1998 by
Wise Publications

Printed in Great Britain by Printwise (Haverhill) Limited, Suffolk

Wise Publications
London/New York/Paris/Sydney/Copenhagen/Madrid

3 Lions '98

Music by Ian Broudie. Words by David Baddiel & Frank Skinner.

We can dance Nob-by's dance,— we could dance it in France.—

It's com - ing home,— it's com - ing, foot-ball's com-ing home,— it's com - ing home,—

—— It's com - ing home,— it's com - ing, foot-ball's com-ing home,— it's com - ing home,—

Repeat and fade

Verse 2:
Talk about football coming home
And then one night in Rome
We were strong, we had grown
And now I see Ince ready for war
Gazza good as before
Shearer ready to score
And Psycho screaming.

La Copa de la Vida

Words & Music by Robi Rosa, Desmond Child & Luis Gomez Escolar.

Verse 2:

La vida es competición
Hay, que soñar ser campeón
La copa es, la bendición
La ganarás, go, go, goal.
Tu instinto natural, vencer a tu rival
Tienes que pelear, por un estrella
Consigue con honor, la Copa del amor
Para sobrevivir, luchar por ella
Luchar por ella, luchar por ella. (Si!)

Tu y yo! etc.

Verse 2:

The cup of life it's do or die
It's here, it's now turn up the lights
Push it along, then let it roll
Push it along, go, go, goal.
And when you feel the heat the world is at your feet
No one can hold you down if you really want it
Just steal your destiny from the hands of fate
Reach for the cup of life 'cause your name is on it.
Do you really want it? (Yeah!) Do you really want it? (Yeah!)

Here we go! etc.

Abide With Me

Words & Music by Henry Lyte & William Monk.

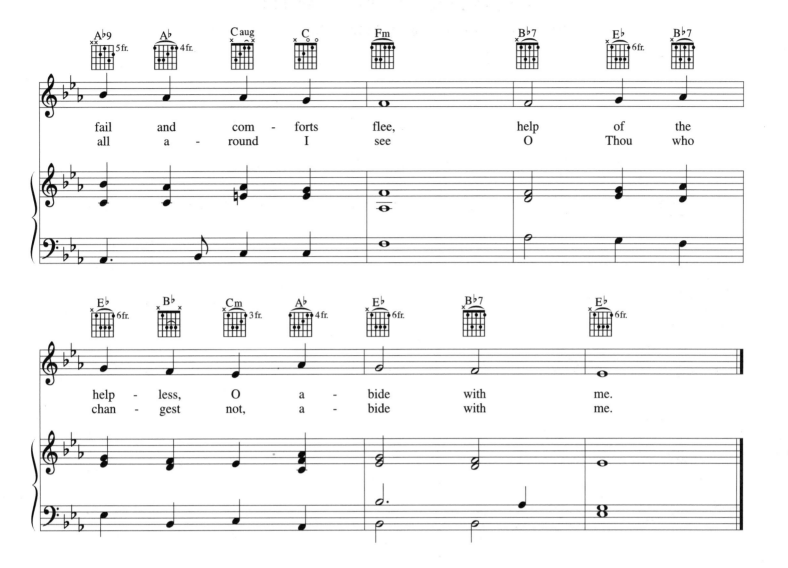

3. I need Thy presence every passing hour
   What but Thy grace can foil the tempter's power?
   Who like Thyself my guide and stay can be?
   Through cloud and sunshine, O abide with me.

4. I fear no foe, with Thee at hand to bless
   Ills have no weight, and tears no bitterness
   Where is death's sting? Where, grave, thy victory?
   I triumph still, if Thou abide with me.

5. Reveal Thyself before my closing eyes
   Shine through the gloom, and point me to the skies
   Heaven's morning breaks, and earth's vain shadows flee
   In life, in death, O Lord, abide with me.

Grandstand (Theme)

By Keith Mansfield.

Nessun Dorma (from Turandot)

By Giacomo Puccini.

-prà! No, no, sol-la tua boc — -ca lo di - rò————— quan-do la

lu — ce splen-de - rà!———— Ed il mio

ba - cio scioglie-rà il si - len - zio———— che ti fa mi - a!

Pavane (BBC World Cup '98 Theme)

Composed by Gabriel Fauré, words by Robert de Montesquiou. Arranged by Elizabeth Scott.

Faites at - ten - tion! Ob - ser - ver la me - sure, nous se - rons leur ca - quets!
Take heed! Fol - low the mea - sure, we shall soon be the subject of their gossip!

Qu'ils sont laid! Et chers mi - nois! Qu'ils sont fols! Airs co - quets!
How ugly their dear little fa - ces are! How fool - ish their co - quet - tish airs!

C'est tou - jours de meme, c'est ain - si tou - jours.
And it is always thus, it is al - ways the same.

Ski Sunday Theme (Pop Looks Bach)

By Sam Fonteyn.

Soul Limbo (BBC Cricket Theme)

By Booker T. Jones, Steve Cropper, Al Jackson & Donald 'Duck' Dunn.

Repeat to fade

Swing Low, Sweet Chariot

Traditional.

The Chain (Grand Prix Theme)

**Words & Music by Lindsey Buckingham, John McVie,
Christine McVie, Mick Fleetwood & Stevie Nicks.**

Repeat to fade

40

Vindaloo

Words & Music by Keith Allen, Guy Pratt & Alex James.

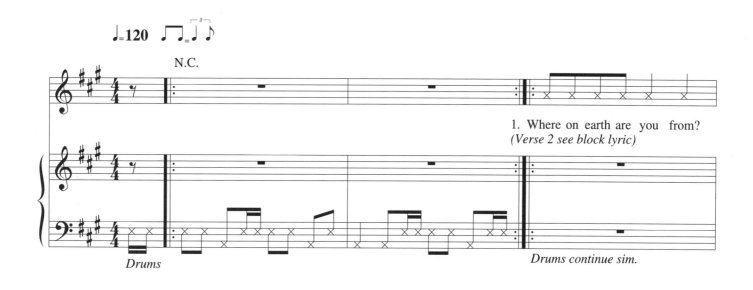

1. Where on earth are you from?
(Verse 2 see block lyric)

Drums continue sim.

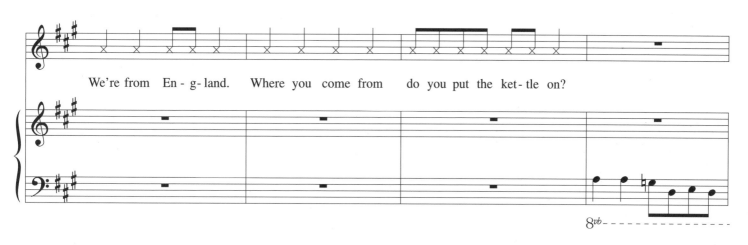

We're from En - g - land. Where you come from do you put the ket - tle on?

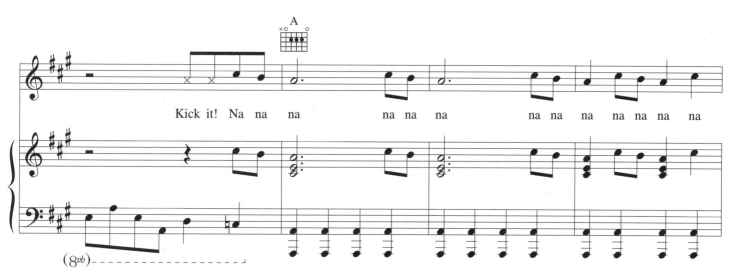

Kick it! Na na na na na na na na na na na na na na

-loo, vin-da-loo, na na. Vin-da-loo, vin-da-loo, and we

all like vin-da-loo. We're En-g-land

We're gon-na score one

more than you. Eng-land! Na na na na na

Vin-da-loo,

na vin-da-loo. na na na vin-da-loo na na. Na na na na na

Vin-da-loo,

Verse 2:
Can I introduce you please
To a lump of cheddar cheese?
Knit one, purl one
Drop one, curl one.

Kick it! Na na na *etc.*

You'll Never Walk Alone

Music by Richard Rodgers. Words by Oscar Hammerstein II.

10/98 (32163)